Better English

AGE 7-9

Rhona Whiteford and Jim Fitzsimmons
Illustrated by Sascha Lipscomb

As a parent, your encouragement and involvement can make an important contribution to your child's education. This book is designed to help your child build on the English skills that they have learned at infant school. It will help your child to develop fluency in reading and to learn the simple rules of grammar, punctuation and spelling. There are five tests to help assess your child's progress.

How to help your child

- Keep sessions short and regular. A short period of work every day is usually more effective than a long session once a week.

- Build your child's confidence by offering lots of praise and encouragement. Rather than simply pointing out that an answer is wrong, you could say, 'You were almost right. Let's try again together!'

- As the spoken word is a vital part of learning a language, always discuss what you are doing together and encourage your child to listen and take turns in conversation.

- Don't treat the tests too formally. They are designed to make your child aware of their progress and give them a sense of achievement. You could keep a running total of their results separately and use this to encourage your child.

Hodder Children's Books

The only home learning programme supported by the NCPTA

Sentences

A **sentence** is a group of words which makes complete sense on its own.

A. Tick the groups of words which make complete sense on their own.
The first two have been done for you.

1. **the sky is blue today** ✓

2. **this car is** ✗

3. **Sam fell off his bicycle** ✓

4. **my brother has** ✗

5. **I like this book** ✓

6. **blue is my** ✗

Sentences always begin with a capital letter and end with a full stop (.), a question mark (**?**) or an exclamation mark (**!**).

B. Re-write these sentences with capital letters and full stops:

1. **sally was upset when she lost her book**

▶ Sally was upset when she lost her book.

2. **the mechanic repaired the car quickly**

▶

3. **the boy was pleased to win the prize**

▶

A sentence which asks something ends with a question mark (**?**). A question can be just one word, e.g. What? Who? When? Why? How? Where? Which?

C. Put a question mark at the end of the sentences below which ask questions:

1. **Where are you going**

2. **This hat is mine**

3. **Who would like cake**

4. **Is this your book**

This is an **exclamation mark - !** It is used to show strong feelings such as surprise, laughter, happiness, fear, pain or anger. An exclamation can be just one word, e.g. Help! Ouch!

A. Write two more one word exclamations.

1.  !   2.  !

B. Put in an exclamation mark where it is needed in the sentences below:

1. As he fell in the pond the boy cried out "Help"

2. The children were making lots of noise

3. When the rocket exploded, everyone shouted "Oooh"

C. Put a full stop, question mark or exclamation mark at the end of each of the following sentences:

1. Where have you left the car ?

2. The garden looks really beautiful .

3. The fireman shouted, "Get out now "

4. I really like strawberries and cream .

5. As the ball hit him, he yelled, "Ouch , "

6. Which is your umbrella ?

Sentences

Complete these sentences by joining the two halves which go best together:

1. The boy took — full of beautiful flowers.

2. The bus driver — my favourite sweets.

3. Chocolates are — his dog for a walk.

4. The park was — stopped at the bus stop.

Conjunctions

Words which are used to join short sentences together are called conjunctions, e.g. and, but, as, for, or, yet, then, before, so, which, because, when, after.

A. Use one of the above conjunctions to join these sentences:

1. Sally got up early _____ she had to catch the train.

2. I wanted a shower _____ the water was too cold.

3. He had his breakfast _____ he went for a long walk.

4. I went out to play _____ I had finished my homework.

5. The alarm did not ring _____ he was late for school.

6. He put up his umbrella _____ he went out in the rain.

Sentences can have different purposes:

A statement	is a sentence which states a fact, e.g. It is very hot.
A question	is a sentence which asks for an answer, e.g. Is it cold outside?
A command	is a sentence which gives an order, e.g. Turn the page.
An exclamation	is a sentence which shows a strong feeling or emotion, e.g. Ouch, that hurt!
A greeting	is a sentence which is used to pass on good wishes, e.g. Good afternoon.

B. Write in each box the kind of sentences you think these are:

1. This is the biggest marrow in the show. ▶

2. Please pick up that litter. ▶

3. When does the show start? ▶

4. Many happy returns. ▶

5. Help, get me out of here! ▶

6. This shop sells flowers. ▶

7. What is your address? ▶

8. Good morning. ▶

Test 1

Tick the correct sentences:

❶ I can see the castle. ☐

❷ Please could you ☐

❸ The dog was hungry. ☐

Re-write these sentences with capital letters and full stops:

❹ i am going away on holiday tomorrow

▶ ______________________________

❺ the painting of flowers won first prize

▶ ______________________________

Put in the correct punctuation below:

❻ "Come here now ☐ "

❼ My favourite food is pizza ☐

❽ "Did you see that space film last night ☐ "

Join the following sentences with a conjunction:

❾ I could see the village ☐ the mist cleared.

❿ Mary washed the dishes ☐ I dried them.

Write which kind of sentence each of these is in the box provided.

⓫ Keep off the grass. ☐

⓬ This car is an old wreck. ☐

SCORE

/12

Nouns

Nouns are words that name people, places and things, e.g. man, house, town, apple.

A. Write out the nouns in each of these sentences.

1. This apple is ripe and juicy.

2. The water was frozen solid.

3. The cat was very hungry.

4. The shop was full of toys.

Proper Nouns - always have a capital letter and are the name of a particular person, place or thing, e.g. London, John, Mercedes.

Common Nouns - do not have capital letters unless they begin a sentence, e.g. book, dog, car.

Sort these words into common and proper nouns. Write each one in the correct column.

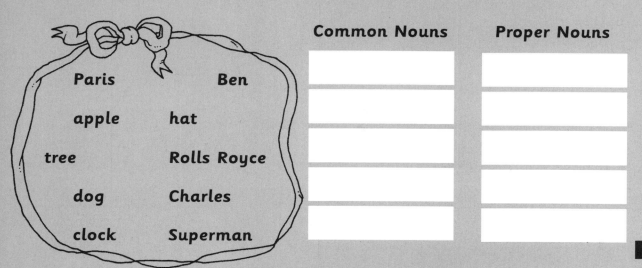

	Common Nouns	Proper Nouns
Paris		
Ben		
apple		
hat		
tree		
Rolls Royce		
dog		
Charles		
clock		
Superman		

Collective Nouns

A **collective noun** is the name of a group of people or things which are all of one kind, e.g. a flock of birds, a bunch of flowers.

Complete these lines using one of the words given in this box.

| fish |
| roses   cattle |

Add one letter to each word below to make a collective noun.

1. A herd of _____

2. A bed of _____

3. A shoal of _____

4. A ___warm of bees

5. A crow___ of people

6. An arm___ of soldiers

Pronouns

A word which takes the place of a noun in a sentence is a **pronoun**. Commonly used pronouns are - I, we, me, us, you, he, she, it, they, him, her, them. **Possessive pronouns** are - mine, yours, ours, his, hers, its, theirs.

A. Rewrite these sentences using a <u>pronoun</u> to avoid repeating the noun, e.g.
The boy cried out when the boy fell.   The boy cried out when <u>he</u> fell.

1. **Sally said that Sally was going to be late.**

▶ _____

2. **We asked Tom and Jane if Tom and Jane were coming.**

▶ _____

B. Use a possessive pronoun to make these sentences shorter:

1. **This coat belongs to him.**   **This coat is** _____

2. **This house belongs to me.**   **This house is** _____

Adjectives

An **adjective** is a word which describes a noun, it tells us what it is like, e.g. a beautiful face, a cloudy day.

A. Underline the adjective in each phrase:

1. a thrilling race

2. the funny clown

3. a stormy night

4. the haunted castle

5. the wild animal

B. Write an adjective to go with these nouns:

1. a _____ snake

2. a _____ book

3. a _____ sea

Write a noun to go with each adjective below:

4. This huge _____

5. The identical _____

6. The delicious _____

C. Write in the space below, the best adjective to describe each noun given, using those provided in the box below.

1. She is a _____ film actress.

2. The _____ farmer chased after us.

3. The _____ dog growled and barked.

4. The acrobat wore a _____ costume.

5. There was a _____ monster in the film.

| angry | famous | ferocious | slimy | sparkling |

Verbs

Verbs can tell us what a person or thing is doing, e.g. He played the piano.

A. Circle the correct verb from the brackets:

1. The children (smiled/ knocked/ ran) at the door.

2. Laura was (swimming/ painting/ sleeping) in her bed.

3. The caretaker was (smashing/ cleaning/ eating) the windows.

Some verbs are words of being, such as <u>am, is, are</u>, e.g. I am in the garden.

B. Write the verbs <u>am, is</u> or <u>are</u> in the blanks to complete the sentence:

1. Mother _____ in the sitting room.   2. I _____ seven years old.

3. _____ you a member of the football team?

Word Families

To use verbs in different ways we change the ending e.g. He <u>looks</u>, She <u>looked</u>, I am <u>look</u>ing. A group of verbs which all share the same root, e.g. <u>look</u>, is called a word family.

I. Complete these word families by adding the endings shown:

Root verb	add 's'	add 'ed'	add 'ing'
laugh			
pull			
act			

Adverbs

Adverbs tell us more about the verb in a sentence. They describe how actions are done, e.g. Peter <u>walked</u> <u>quickly</u>. The adverb, <u>quickly</u>, tells us how Peter walked.   (verb)   (adverb)

A. Draw a line under the verb, and a ring around the adverb in each sentence.

1. I listened carefully.

3. The car stopped suddenly.

2. He shouted angrily.

4. The engine rattled noisily.

Adverbs are made by adding **ly** to an adjective, e.g. quick (adjective) becomes quickly (adverb). If an adjective ends in the letter **y** it becomes an adverb by adding **il** in front of the **y**, e.g. sleepy (adjective) becomes sleepily (adverb).

B. Complete each sentence with an adverb, made from the adjective on the left.

1. clear   We could see _____ from the cliff top.

2. careful   The children crossed the road _____ .

3. quiet   We crept _____ into the library.

4. soft   The cat landed _____ on the grass.

5. brave   The fireman fought the fire _____ .

6. happy   The children smiled _____ for the

photographer.

■ TEST 2 ■

① Underline the nouns in these sentences:

a) The dog chased after the cat. b) The boat sailed away over the sea.

② Write two common nouns below:

a) ▶ [   ]   b) ▶ [   ]

③ Write two proper nouns below:

a) ▶ [   ]   b) ▶ [   ]

④ Fill in the gaps below with the right collective noun:

a) A [   ] of bees   b) A [   ] of people

⑤ Underline the pronouns in these sentences:

a) The gardener promised he would cut the grass.

b) This coat is hers.

⑥ Underline the adjectives in these sentences:

a) We watched an exciting film. b) The scruffy dog rolled in the grass.

⑦ Underline the verbs in these sentences:

a) The policeman stopped the car. b) I am the son of a doctor.

⑧ Make adverbs from these adjectives:

a) noisy ▶ [   ]   b) graceful ▶ [   ]

⑨ Add a verb with the right ending to make sense of the sentences below:

a) I always [   ] to school. b) I [   ] my tea quickly this
afternoon.

⑩ Write out the word family for the verb <u>talk</u>:

SCORE

/ 10

Commas

This is a **comma - ,**. We use it when there is a list of words in a sentence. We separate each word with a comma. The last word in the list is usually joined to it by the word <u>and</u> instead of a comma, e.g. We need paper, paint, glue <u>and</u> scissors.

A. Put commas in these sentences:

1. At the zoo we saw lions tigers monkeys and elephants.

2. There was a huge pile of hats coats scarves shoes and socks.

3. The colours of the rainbow are red orange yellow green blue indigo and violet.

The comma can also be used to mark a short pause inside a sentence. It is used to separate two words, or groups of words, in a sentence, to make the meaning clearer, e.g. After we had been to the park, we went to the café.

B. Put a comma in these sentences:

1. Once the box was opened we could see inside.

2. The window was smashed to pieces when the ball hit the glass.

3. With all the heavy rain the garden was flooded.

Apostrophes

A comma written above the line is called an **apostrophe**. We can use an apostrophe to show that some letters have been missed out, e.g. Do not = Don't, We are = We're, What is = What's, You will = You'll, I will = I'll, I am = I'm.

A. Write the shortened form of these words by leaving out the letters underlined and putting in an apostrophe instead. The first one has been done for you.

1. let <u>us</u> ▶ let's

2. we <u>had</u> ▶

3. can<u>no</u>t ▶

4. it <u>is</u> ▶

5. we <u>will</u> ▶

6. I <u>have</u> ▶

7. should <u>have</u> ▶

8. could n<u>o</u>t ▶

9. has n<u>o</u>t ▶

10. would n<u>o</u>t ▶

11. did n<u>o</u>t ▶

12. have n<u>o</u>t ▶

13. we <u>a</u>re ▶

14. she <u>is</u> ▶

An apostrophe can be used to show something belongs to someone.

If there is only one owner of an object, we add the apostrophe and **s** to show something belongs, e.g. John's coat.	When there is a group of people - <u>the boys</u> - owning a set of things - <u>coats</u> - the apostrophe comes after the **s** or **es**, e.g. The boys' coats.

B. Put in the apostrophe below:

1. Sally s bag.

2. Father s chair.

3. The girl s hat.

4. The cats baskets.

5. The ladies hats.

6. The ships sails.

Inverted commas

There are two ways of writing down what someone says. If we write down the exact words spoken it is called **direct speech**. If we repeat what they said in our own words it is called **indirect speech**.
e.g. Fred said, "I am late."   Fred said that he was late.
(Direct speech)   (Indirect speech)

A. Put a ring around the sentences in direct speech and underline those in indirect speech:

1. Jack said that he really liked his present.

2. May I go out to play? asked Ben.

3. What time is it? asked Alex.

4. Mum asked me if I would go to the shops.

Words that are actually spoken are written inside inverted commas, also known as speech marks or quotation marks. These (") go at the beginning of the speech, and these (") go at the end. The spoken words start with a capital letter, e.g. " These are my gloves," said Pam.

B. Draw a ring around the words which are actually spoken, then re-write the sentence using inverted commas.

1.   I am going out to play, said Helen.

▶   "I am going out to play," said Helen.

2.   This is my favourite game, said Lynne.

▶

3.   I like watching television, said Roger.

▶

TEST 3

Put commas in the following sentences:

① On the motorway we saw cars lorries buses and wagons.

② At the stationery shop I bought pencils paper rubbers and glue.

③ In the circus parade we saw clowns acrobats jugglers and animals.

④ We had lunch then we went shopping.

⑤ Before going to bed I had a bath.

Put the apostrophes in below:

⑥ Sam s dog

⑦ Mother s hat

⑧ Mary s car

⑨ Tom s book

⑩ Grandmother s shawl

⑪ the babies prams

⑫ the footballers shirts

⑬ the ladies handbags

⑭ the boys pencils

⑮ the soldiers uniforms

Put in the inverted commas where they are needed:

⑯ May I come to the party too? asked William.

⑰ Sarah said that she had lost her favourite book.

⑱ It is my birthday today, said the old man.

⑲ The shopkeeper said, I am closing early tomorrow.

⑳ The doctor told the patient that he was much better.

SCORE

20

16

Singular or plural

A **singular** word talks about one thing or one group, e.g. one cow or one herd of cows. There are many spelling rules for changing a word from singular to plural. A **plural** talks about many things or groups of things.

A simple rule. Most words just add 's', e.g. cat changes to cats.

1. Write the plural of these words:

doctor _____   tree _____   hose _____   flute _____

Words ending in s, x, ch, tch, sh, add 'es', e.g. bus changes to buses.

2. Make these words plural:

fox _____   brush _____   match _____   torch _____

church _____   kiss _____   watch _____   peach _____

Words ending in y. If there is a vowel before the 'y' add 's'. If there is a consonant before the 'y' change 'y' to 'i' and add 'es', e.g. puppy becomes puppies.

3. Write the plural of these words:

army _____   tray _____   toy _____

cherry _____   quay _____   memory _____

Words ending in f or fe. Most f and fe words add 'ves', e.g. leaf changes to leaves. Remember ff words always add 's'.

4. Change these words to the plural:

wolf _____   cliff _____   wife _____

calf _____   ruff _____   knife _____

Silent letters

'h' is often silent after a 'w', e.g. <u>wh</u>ale

Put the silent 'h' in the spaces below to complete the words:

w__en   w__ether   w__at   w__ere   w__im

w__y   w__ile   w__ite   w__ich   w__elk

'h' is also silent after a 'g', e.g. g<u>h</u>ost.
Sometimes both letters are silent, e.g. nig<u>ht</u>.

Add gh to the gaps below and draw a line to match with the right clue.

1. hi__   **The opposite of dark**

2. si__   **A girl child is a _____**

3. bri__t   **A light breath.**

4. dau__ter   **Opposite of dull.**

5. li__t   **Opposite of low.**

Shade in the silent letter of the words below. Write another word in each
box, using the same silent letters e.g. calf and half.

calf	comb	wren	know	gnat	rhythm
l f	m b	w r	k n	g n	r h

Double letters

We sometimes use double letters to spell a single sound e.g. se**ll**, cli**ff**. They usually appear after a short vowel sound e.g. pa**tt**er, sme**ll**, mi**ll**, cro**ss**, su**pp**er, but not after a long vowel sound e.g. g**a**te, f**ee**t, m**i**le, b**o**ne, l**u**te.

1. Write two more words using these double letters:

'll'
fell

'pp'
happy

'ff'
whiff

'ss'
bless

2. Pick the correct spelling for these words:

bu ____ (z / zz)

fu ____ y (n / nn)

a ____ ear (p / pp)

bee ____ (f / ff)

bu ____ le (b / bb)

usua ____ y (l / ll)

Hard or soft sounds

'c' can be soft and sound like 's', as in cinema, or hard as in cake.
'g' can be soft and sound like 'j', as in gym, or hard as in get.

Write 'h' for hard or 's' for soft next to these words:

general

cygnet

ceiling

cable

gesture

gun

gone

cattle

gentle

cement

Write 3 words for each in the columns below:

soft 'c'

soft 'g'

■ TEST 4 ■

Write the plurals of these words:

1 wolf ▶ [ ]   **2** cake ▶ [ ]

3 chicken ▶ [ ]   **4** berry ▶ [ ]

5 sash ▶ [ ]   **6** country ▶ [ ]

Write the singular of these words:

7 boxes ▶ [ ]   **8** watches ▶ [ ]

9 memories ▶ [ ]   **10** knives ▶ [ ]

11 pigs ▶ [ ]   **12** churches ▶ [ ]

Use the clue to find a word using the silent letters given:

13 A medieval soldier ▶ [ ]   kn

14 A broken ship ▶ [ ]   wr

15 Fixes burst pipes ▶ [ ]   mb

Double Letters. Unravel the letters to find a word:

16 lifcf ▶ [ ]

17 aphpy ▶ [ ]

18 sems ▶ [ ]

SCORE

/18

Joined-up handwriting

Joined-up handwriting helps you learn to spell! The flow and joined pattern helps fix the **letter string** in your mind.

Practise these strings in your school style.

ight ide dge age tion aught aught

Letter strings

Letter strings are letters that appear grouped together in different words and always sound the same, e.g. -ight, -dge, -ought.

tion as in station

Add the letter string, then write the whole word.

1. ac_____

2. por_____   *tion*

3. ra_____

age and *dge*, as in marriage and ledge, are found at the end of words.

Sort these words out:

age	*dge*

hedge   passage
    voyage
judge   bridge
    manage
wedge   damage
    sausage

More letter strings

able as in sta<u>ble</u>. Fill in the missing words below:

1. A plant we eat is a   v _ _ _ _ _ _ _ _

2. A place to keep a horse is a   s I A B L E

3. We sit at a   t A B L E   to eat.

4. We are   c _ _ _ _ _ _ _ _ _   when we feel restful and cosy.

ight as in night is a common word ending.

Make word crosses for these words ending in -ight.

knight
sight
light
might
tonight
right

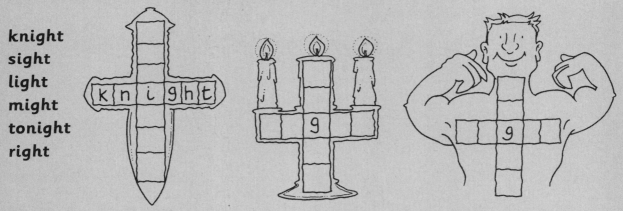

ought and *aught* usually sound the same and we simply have to remember when each is used.

Sort these words into the right columns according to their endings:

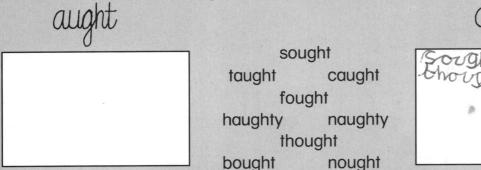

aught

ought

sought

taught   caught

fought

haughty   naughty

thought

bought   nought

Sought bought thought

Beginnings

Sometimes a group of letters is added to the beginning of a word to change its meaning. This is called a **prefix**. Adding a prefix is easy, there is no need to drop any letters, e.g. mis + spell = misspell. The odd ones out are all and well which drop an l when they are added to the beginning of a word, e.g. all + together = altogether and well + come = welcome.

Opposites

Some prefixes change a word to its opposite meaning.
Match these prefixes to the words below to change their meaning:

PREFIXES

mis	dis	un
non	in	im

WORDS

take	appoint	do
sense	expensive	proper

Now list the new words you have made:

1. ▶
2. ▶
3. ▶
4. ▶
5. ▶
6. ▶

Add some of the prefixes suggested above to the words in the following passage to change the meaning:

I had been the most ...... obedient child in class all term. My teacher thought it ...... likely that the headteacher would reward me for my ..... behaviour. My mother agreed that that would be ...... possible.

NUMBER PREFIXES

uni	-	one
bi	-	two
tri	-	three
poly	-	many
multi	-	many

Draw a line to match each prefix with the words on the right.

uni	-angle
bi	-gon
tri	-coloured
poly	-cycle
multi	- corn

Endings

Some suffixes change the way a verb can be used, e.g. talk + <u>ed</u> = talk<u>ed</u>. This changes I talk (present tense) to I talk<u>ed</u> (past tense). (see Word Families on page 10.)

Choose the right verb ending to make sense of the sentences below:

a) Mum (smile/ smiles/ smiling) when she sees me.
b) We (visit/ visits/ visited) my friend today.
c) My family (enjoys/ enjoyed/ enjoying) going to the cinema.

Some suffixes change a word into an adjective.

WORD	SUFFIX	NEW WORD (ADJECTIVE)	SENTENCE
fright ⟶	ful ⟶	frightful	He looks frightful
care ⟶	less		
self ⟶	ish		
delight ⟶	ful		

Some suffixes change a word into a type of noun.

<u>Suffix</u>	Add the correct suffix to complete the sentences.
-er	1. There is great friend............ within the team.
-hood	2. Our swimming teach............ is great.
-ship	3. My dad started a neighbour............ watch scheme.

Unusual words

Homophones are words which have a different spelling and a different meaning from each other but often sound the same.

Can you write the meanings for each of these homophones below?

1. boy - | a male child |

   buoy - | a floating marker |

2. key - | |

   quay - | |

3. hair - | |

   hare - | |

4. pain - | |

   pane - | |

Fill the gaps in these sentences with the correct homophone:

5. I can WRITE very neatly. (write / right)

6. I'd love a PIECE of cake. (piece / peace)

7. I quickly let go of the _____ . (rein / reign)

Homonyms are words which have a different meaning from each other but are spelt and sound the same, e.g. a lighted match, a football match.

Write two sentences for each of these words to show the different meanings:

watch
1. ▶
2. ▶

light
1. ▶
2. ▶

hatch
1. ▶
2. ▶

LETTER STRINGS. The three answers below share the same letter string. Guess the word and write it out in joined-up handwriting:

❶ Opposite of left [   ]   **❷** Opposite of loose [   ]

❸ Opposite of depth [   ]

PREFIXES. Change these words to their opposite meaning by adding a prefix:

❹ sense ▶[   ]   **❺** do ▶[   ]

❻ like ▶[   ]

SUFFIXES. Add a suffix to these verbs to make a noun which means a worker doing each of these jobs:

❼ paint ▶[   ]   **❽** farm ▶[   ]

❾ engine ▶[   ]

HOMOPHONES. These words sound the same but only one is spelt right for the sentence. Underline the right words below:

❿ The owl hooted outside the window all knight / night.

⓫ The doctor said she needed to way / weigh me.

⓬ I am learning to sew / so.

HOMONYMS. There are two meanings for each of these words. Write a sentence for each of them:

⓭ train [   ] [   ]

⓮ mould [   ] [   ]

⓯ flat [   ] [   ]

SCORE

[/ 15]

26

Finding information

We store information in computers, books, directories, dictionaries, encyclopaedias and libraries and we store this information alphabetically. This means we need to know the alphabet to find the information in these places.

A. Quickly fill in the missing letters:

A B _ _ _ E F _ H _ _ _ K L M _ _ _ P Q _ S _ U _ W X _ Z

a _ _ _ d _ _ f g _ _ i j _ _ l m n _ _ _ _ _ r s _ _ u v _ _ x y _ _

B. Use a dictionary to find:

3 words starting with 'M'

▶
▶
▶

3 five letter words

▶
▶
▶

The longest word you can find: ▶

C. Look in your telephone directory to find:

1. **The phone number of a toy shop.** ▶

2. **The phone number of a relative or friend.** ▶

D. Look in the index of your favourite topic book to find three interesting items:

Book:	Item 1 --- page ---
	Item 2 --- page ---
	Item 3 --- page ---

Reading with understanding

Read the passage below then answer the questions about it.

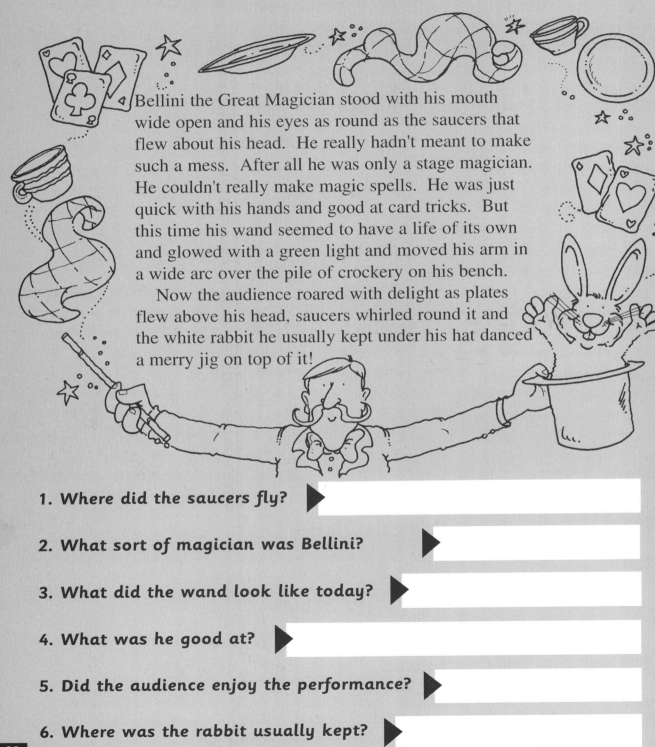

Bellini the Great Magician stood with his mouth wide open and his eyes as round as the saucers that flew about his head. He really hadn't meant to make such a mess. After all he was only a stage magician. He couldn't really make magic spells. He was just quick with his hands and good at card tricks. But this time his wand seemed to have a life of its own and glowed with a green light and moved his arm in a wide arc over the pile of crockery on his bench.

Now the audience roared with delight as plates flew above his head, saucers whirled round it and the white rabbit he usually kept under his hat danced a merry jig on top of it!

1. **Where did the saucers fly?**

2. **What sort of magician was Bellini?**

3. **What did the wand look like today?**

4. **What was he good at?**

5. **Did the audience enjoy the performance?**

6. **Where was the rabbit usually kept?**

Reading with care

Some words have been left out of the passage. In some cases only one word will do to make it read correctly, but in other cases you can choose from several words to give the writing a new meaning.

Read through the passage quickly to get an idea of the meaning, then read more carefully, trying out some of the words listed in the box below. When you are satisfied with your choice, write it in the spaces below and read the passage through again.

The visitors

Slowly and steadily the -------------- craft settled just above ------------ level

and hovered there silently. A doorway materialized -------------- the side and

from it -------------- a shimmering ramp. From their hiding place behind the

bushes, the children stared in ------------------ as two circles of light appeared at

the doorway and moved down the ramp ------------------. As they moved they

formed into figures, small but of -------------- shape and with the most -----------

faces. It was obvious that ------------- planet was strange and new to them.

They -------------------- around with wondering eyes and, holding hands,

---------------- stepped on to the grass. The children gasped as the creatures

looked in ---------------- direction and, smiling, moved towards ----------------

bushes with arms outstretched in greeting.

The words in the box are arranged in the same order as the spaces in the passage. Where you have a choice, suggested words are grouped together but you may use your own ideas if you want to.

space	alien		ground	roof		in
stretched	shot	glided	terror	astonishment	horror
together	slowly	silently	human	strange	alien
beautiful	terrible	unusual	this		
looked	glared	stared	they	their	the

Answers

Page 2

A. 1, 3 and 5 form sentences.

B. 1. Sally was upset when she lost her book.
2. The mechanic repaired the car quickly.
3. The boy was pleased to win the prize.

C. 1. Where are you going?
3. Who would like cake?
4. Is this your book?

Page 3

B. 1. As he fell in the pond the boy cried out "Help!"
2. The children were making lots of noise.
3. When the rocket exploded, everyone shouted "Oooh!"

C. 1. Where have you left the car?
2. The garden looks really beautiful.
3. The fireman shouted, "Get out now!"
4. I really like strawberries and cream.
5. As the ball hit him, he yelled, "Ouch!"
6. Which is your umbrella?

Page 4

1. The boy took his dog for a walk.
2. The bus driver stopped at the bus stop.
3. Chocolates are my favourite sweets.
4. The park was full of beautiful flowers.

A. 1. because/as 2. but
3. before/then
4. when/after
5. so
6. when/before

(There are different alternatives for some of the above answers - at the marker's discretion)

Page 5

B. 1. Statement
2. Command
3. Question
4. Greeting
5. Exclamation
6. Statement
7. Question
8. Greeting

Page 6

TEST 1

1 & 3 are correct sentences.
4. I am going away on holiday tomorrow.
5. The painting of flowers won first prize.
6. "Come here now!"
7. My favourite food is pizza.
8. "Did you see that space film last night?"
9. I could see the village when/after the mist cleared.
10. Mary washed the dishes so/as/while/then/and I dried them.
11. Command
12. Statement

Page 7

A. 1. apple 2. water
3. cat   4. shop, toys

Common Nouns - apple, tree, dog, clock, hat

Proper Nouns - Paris, Ben, Rolls Royce, Charles, Superman

Page 8

1. cattle 2. roses 3. fish
4. swarm 5. crowd
6. army

A. 1. Sally said that she was going to be late.
2. We asked Tom and Jane if they were coming.

B. 1. This coat is his.
2. This house is mine.

Page 9

A. 1. thrilling   2. funny
3. stormy
4. haunted 5. wild

C. 1. famous   2. angry
3. ferocious
4. sparkling 5. slimy

Page 10

A. 1. knocked 2. sleeping
3. cleaning

B. 1. is 2. am 3. are

1. laughs, laughed, laughing
pulls, pulled, pulling
acts, acted, acting

Page 11

A. 1. listened (verb) carefully (adverb)
   2. shouted (verb) angrily (adverb)
   3. stopped (verb) suddenly (adverb)
   4. rattled (verb) noisily (adverb)

B. 1. clearly   2. carefully
   3. quietly   4. softly
   5. bravely   6. happily

Page 12

TEST 2
1a) dog, cat   1b) boat, sea
4a) swarm   4b) crowd
5a) he   5b) hers
6a) exciting   6b) scruffy
7a) stopped   7b) am
8a) noisily   8b) gracefully
10. talk, talks, talked, talking

Page 13

A. 1. At the zoo we saw lions, tigers, monkeys and elephants.
   2. There was a huge pile of hats, coats, scarves, shoes and socks.
   3. The colours of the rainbow are red, orange, yellow, green, blue, indigo and violet.

B. 1. Once the box was opened, we could see inside.
   2. The window was smashed to pieces, when the ball hit the glass.
   3. With all the heavy rain, the garden was flooded.

Page 14

A. 1. let's   2. we'd
   3. can't   4. it's
   5. we'll   6. I've
   7. should've
   8. couldn't
   9. hasn't   10. wouldn't
   11. didn't   12. haven't
   13. we're   14. she's

B. 1. Sally's   2. Father's
   3. girl's   4. cats'
   5. ladies'   6. ships'

Page 15

A. 1 & 4 - indirect
   2 & 3 - direct
   "May I go out to play?" asked Ben.
   "What time is it?" asked Alex.

B. 2. "This is my favourite game," said Lynne.
   3. "I like watching television," said Roger.

Page 16

TEST 3
1. On the motorway we saw cars, lorries, buses and wagons.
2. At the stationery shop I bought pencils, paper, rubbers and glue.
3. In the circus parade we saw clowns, acrobats, jugglers and animals.
4. We had lunch, then we went shopping.
5. Before going to bed, I had a bath.

6. Sam's dog
7. Mother's hat
8. Mary's car
9. Tom's book
10. Grandmother's shawl
11. the babies' prams
12. the footballers' shirts
13. the ladies' handbags
14. the boys' pencils
15. the soldiers' uniforms
16. "May I come to the party too?" asked William.
17. Sarah said that she had lost her favourite book.
18. "It is my birthday today," said the old man.
19. The shopkeeper said, "I am closing early tomorrow."
20. The doctor told the patient that he was much better.

Page 17

1. doctors, trees, hoses, flutes
2. foxes, brushes, matches, torches, churches, kisses, watches, peaches
3. armies, trays, toys, cherries, quays, memories
4. wolves, cliffs, wives, calves, ruffs, knives

Page 18

1. high   2. sigh   3. bright
4. daughter   5. light
silent letters: l, b, w, k, g, h

Page 19

2. buzz, funny, appear, beef, bubble, usually.

Hard sounds - cable, gun, gone, cattle

Soft sounds - general, cygnet, ceiling, gesture, gentle, cement

Page 20
TEST 4
1. wolves
2. cakes
3. chickens
4. berries
5. sashes
6. countries
7. box
8. watch
9. memory
10. knife
11. pig
12. church
13. knight
14. wreck
15. plumber
16. cliff
17. happy
18. mess

Page 22
1. vegetable
2. stable
3. table
4. comfortable

Page 23
mistake, disappoint, undo, nonsense, inexpensive, improper

dis - obedient   un - likely
mis - behaviour
im - possible

unicorn, bicycle, triangle, polygon, multicoloured

Page 24
a) smiles   b) visited
c) enjoys

friendship, teacher, neighbourhood

Page 25
2. key – an instrument for locking or unlocking.
quay – a landing place for boats.
3. hair – a fibre growing from the skin.
hare - a swift mammal, larger than a rabbit.
4. pane – a piece of window glass.
pain – suffering.
5. write
6. piece
7. rein

Page 26
TEST 5
1. right
2. tight
3. height
4. nonsense
5. undo
6. dislike
7. painter
8. farmer
9. engineer
10. night
11. weigh
12. sew
13. steam <u>train</u> or <u>train</u> for athletics
14. <u>mould</u> grew on the ceiling or <u>mould</u> a pot from clay.
15. buy a <u>flat</u> or squash <u>flat</u>.

Page 28
1. about his head
2. stage magician
3. It glowed with a green light.
4. card tricks
5. yes
6. under his hat

ISBN 0 340 64669 1

Copyright © 1995 Rhona Whiteford and Jim Fitzsimmons

The right of Rhona Whiteford and Jim Fitzsimmons to be identified as the authors of this work has been asserted by them in accordance with the Copyright, Design and Patent Act 1988.

First published in Great Britain 1995

10 9 8 7 6 5 4 3 2 1

Published by Hodder Children's Books, a division of Hodder Headline plc, 338 Euston Road, London NW1 3BH.
Printed in Great Britain.

A CIP record is registered by and held at the British Library.